You WeRe MaDe FoR Me

BY **SHERI STURNIOLO**

ILLUSTRATED BY **HANNAH PAK**

For Babe...

To my husband, without you
the puzzle would never be complete

"Where once lay the heart of a woman,
now beats the heart of a mother"
My deepest gratitude to our generous
donors and wonderful doctor

YouWereMadeForMe.com

You Were Made For Me

BY **SHERI STURNIOLO**

ILLUSTRATED BY **HANNAH PAK**

I'll tell you a story, amazing and true,
Of how you became the most wonderful you!

I could never imagine the love that would be,
When I finally knew you were made just for me!

But first is a story that's told just before.
Before you were you.
Before you were more.

Before you were you, and not too long ago,
We were dreaming of you: we were wanting you so!
Dreams of a family and a baby to grow,
A baby to love and a baby to know.

Just like a puzzle with pieces that fit
To make up a baby, you need quite a bit!
Try as we may and try as we might,
We just couldn't make the pieces fit right.

So over and over, we kept trying to try
To fit all the pieces, reaching higher than high.

So out of the house, we finally flew
To ask our wise doctor: *What, oh what, could we do?*

Said the doctor to us, "You have many pieces just right.
But you're missing some shapes to make them fit tight.
I know you are sad," she said with a sigh,
"But there's something amazing, I think we can try."

"There are wonderful, giving people indeed,
Who happen to have just the pieces you need.
The most precious pieces made with love and with care,
These wonderful people are willing to share."

With these last, little pieces put together just so,
You went into Mommy's tummy to grow.
From a dot, to a pea, to a melon you grew,
Bigger than big, 'til the day you were due.

So excited were we. so excited. you see,
To meet our sweet baby and see who you'd be!

You entered the world with a cry then a smile.
And snuggled in Mommy's warm arms for a while.
So precious were you: so happy were we:
Everyone shouted with you, "Yippie!"

The pieces they fit.
The pieces so sweet.
Our dreams had come true.
The puzzle complete.

The story I tell you is truer than true.
The story of us and how you became you.

There's no doubt about it, you were made just for me.
And forever and ever, my baby you'll be!

ABOUT THE AUTHOR

Sheri is a Pediatric Registered Nurse and mother to a son and daughter—children born through the awesome gift of donors. Through her personal journey and experiences, Sheri hopes to offer a valuable tool to families searching for ways to make sense of their unique creation story. Sheri lives with her husband, son and daughter (both conceived through embryo adoption) in the San Diego area.

WRITE YOUR OWN STORY

Use this page to tell your child's creation story:

_____

_____

_____

_____

_____

_____

_____

_____

_____

_____

_____

_____

Made in the USA
San Bernardino, CA
17 May 2019